The Magical Quests

by

Harry Bevan

POLARITY
PUBLISHING

Orders: Please contact Polarity Publishing via the email address: Orders@polaritypublishing.co.uk

ISBN: 978-1-9995810-5-3

First published 2021

Hi, I'm Harry, thank you for buying my book, I am 8 years old and love to create stories in my mind. I have Dyslexia which means that sometimes I find it difficult to write those ideas down. However, I wanted to show myself and other children that no matter how hard something might seem, if you keep working hard and stay focused on your goals, you can achieve whatever you like.

I live at home with my Mum, Dad, Sister and Siberian Forest Cat Oski. I also have 2 older siblings who live in their own homes. For fun I enjoy watching Harry Potter and going to Stagecoach, some of the ideas in The Magical Quests were inspired by JK Rowling's Harry Potter books.

I'd like to thank my Dad, Mum and Sister for helping me write and create The Magical Quest. I hope you enjoy the story.

Contents

Chapter 1 – The School Run

Today I am going to school.

When I think about it, I do not really like school, but once I am there it is quite fun.

But first I must go through the bother of getting ready.

So, I start by having a large breakfast of toast, strawberries, raspberries, grapes, and a Caramel chocolate bar, which is my favourite.

Then I get my uniform on, I put on my clean black trousers and my soft white school shirt.

I brush my teeth for 2 minutes with a very minty toothpaste.

Finally, I put on my shoes, grab my packed lunch, and start my walk to school.

I walk casually, until I see a new building site in front of the way I need to go.

This means I have to go the long way round.

AAARRRGGHH!!!

I stomp angrily to school, after 5 minutes I notice I only have 3 minutes left to get there.

I begin to sprint as fast as I can. It feels faster than a Cheetah, but I'm sure it isn't.

Because I am sprinting so fast, I go the wrong way.

This means I have to swerve around a corner to take a shortcut and squeeze through some bushes.

I am finally at school. I have a few scratches from the bushes, but I am ok.

Chapter 2 – Getting Over the Gate

I check my watch and shout, "Oh no, I'm late, I will have to climb over the locked gate."

Nearby I see an old football, I think that could be useful. As I can stand on the football to help me get over the gate, because the old iron gate is taller than me.

I grab the football and stand on it to help me get over the gate, but it slips out from under my feet.

OOWWWW! I land heavily on my elbow; it feels like an asteroid colliding into a planet.

I think my elbow could be broken. Now I really have a struggle to get over the gate.

I try again, and I manage to get my good arm on top of the gate.

I start to pull myself up, I get one leg over and balance on the top, I'm worried that I might fall back.

My best friend John and his brother suddenly appear behind me.

This catches me by surprise, and I slip back and fall right on top of John.

"Sorry about that John, I hope I haven't hurt you," I say.

We get up and dust ourselves down, and I realise John and his brother Chandler are also late for school.

I ask them, "Why are you delayed?"

The brothers explain that as they walked to school a massive new building site had been in their way too.

So, they were not able to get to school via their normal route.

They are both livid, as they just wanted to get to school on time.

I begin to sense for some odd reason that something very strange is happening.

I say to John and Chandler, "We need to investigate what is going on before things get any weirder."

But first of all we need to get in to school, as we are all now very late.

I get John to stand on my shoulders so he can jump over the gate.

Once John is over the gate, I get Chandler to do the same.

The school side is solid concrete so they both land with quite a bump.

I tell my friends, "I'll jump onto the top of the gate and you both need to pull me over as soon as I reach the top."

I use all my strength and jump up and grab the top of the gate with my good arm.

John and Chandler try to grab me, but it does not work, and I slip back down.

We try again but this time John is on top of Chandler's shoulders.

As soon as I land on the gate, John is able to wrestle me to the school side.

After some huffing and puffing we are finally all the right side of the school gate, and we start to head to class.

Chapter 3 – The Office Walls

Because we are late, we need to go through the school office.

We walk across the playground to the office, as we arrive at the office we knock on the door.

There is no answer, so we just open the door and step into the office.

No one is there, but we hear a creaking noise, and we see the yellow painted wall nearest to us is moving forward.

It keeps moving towards us, getting closer and closer.

We start to get pressed up against the wall behind us and it begins to crush.

John and Chandler managed to jump through a window, but I am left being squashed between the bricks.

I see a door key card out of the corner of my eye.

I can barely reach it, but with one more stretch I managed to get my fingertips on it and grab it.

I continue to be pushed against the wall; I try to open the door but it's too late.

John and Chandler see this and shout, "NNNNOOOOOOOOO!!!!!!" and begin to cry.

They hear me squeal as the wall starts to push heavily against me.

Then suddenly, I start to go through it.

It is a fake wall. It's like a projection.

John and Chandler laugh with joy that I am not crushed, and I deny that I had ever squealed in fear.

Chapter 4 - Meeting Molly

John, Chandler, and I go through the office door to the school and into the hall.

I shout, "Look there's Molly."

Molly asks, "Did you see the school office wall move?"

We all nod and start to tell Molly all about the adventures we have experienced so far on this very strange day.

Molly tells us that when she came to school, the front gate kept opening and closing by itself.

Chandler says, "Guys let's stop chit chatting, we've got to get to class."

Before we move, I feel a strong breeze in the hall.

I look behind me to make sure all four of us are together, we are.

So, I say, "let's go."

As we walk to class the floor behind us starts to crack and disappear, with a loud rumble and bang.

The four of us start to sprint across the hallway and we notice that the bookshelves, paintings, and benches all begin to disappear.

We run as fast as we can towards the door to the playground.

We all dive to reach the heavy wooden door, all the floor behind us has gone, apart from a tiny ledge which we are all holding onto for dear life.

"Why is this happening to us!" Molly screams.

"I don't know, but please somebody help us," Chandler responds.

"What happens if we fall," says John.

In our minds, we all know what's going to happen if we do fall. We will get seriously hurt or even worse.

Directly beneath me I see another much bigger ledge suddenly appear.

I step on the bigger ledge and manage to climb through the door into the school playground.

Chandler shouts, "Help us."

I manage to reach down to Molly and Chandler and pull them up to the safety of the playground.

But I can't reach John, he's too far away.

John screams, "Help, get me up quick, I'm losing my grip."

I shout, "You could let go; you might survive the fall. But I don't think we should risk it."

Molly grabs hold of my feet, and Chandler grabs hold of Molly's feet, and I dangle over the edge to reach John.

I reach down to John, and he grabs on to one of my arms. My arm is really hurting, it's the one I damaged earlier.

I can't handle the pain and John falls, "AAARRRRRGGGGGGGHHHHHHHHH," John screams.

John lands with a big thump as he hits another ledge.

We all breathe a sigh of relief.

Then two more ledges appear, and John starts to climb to safety.

Eventually we all make it safely to the playground.

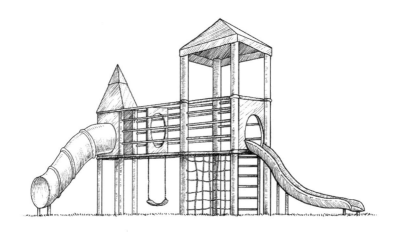

Chapter 5 – Playground Adventures

We start to walk across the playground and the sky begins to darken slowly.

We keep walking towards our Year 6 classroom. Chandler is Year 5 but he tags along. Suddenly there is an almighty clap of thunder and a huge lightning strike.

The lightning strikes the ground directly in front of our classroom door.

Immediately afterwards the rain starts, and I feel drops on my head.

Then it begins pouring down as hard as a waterfall from the top of a cliff.

So, we all ran into the Year 4 classroom, it's empty, and all the tables and chairs have fallen over and are scattered everywhere.

There is a message on the whiteboard written in red. It reads, "Go away or suffer the consequences."

Chandler says in a nervous voice, "It is probably just the Year 4 children playing a trick on us."

Chapter 6 –
The Classroom with
Eyes

We see a black figure looking at us through the classroom window.

The black figure has a large head and wears a long-hooded robe. We can only see its mouth, which is a round circle.

We all tremble and start to edge away from the window and head to our Year 6 classroom.

As we get towards our classroom door, the black figure suddenly appears in front of us.

We immediately turn around and run back to the Year 4 classroom.

Molly notices that the message on the whiteboard has changed.

Leave Now! don't risk suffering the consequences!!

Molly reads aloud, "Leave Now! Don't risk suffering the consequences."

We all desperately want to leave. But we know all our school friends are in trouble.

It was now our quest to find out where everybody had gone.

The writing on the whiteboard begins to change again. Now it reads, "Go to your classroom or I will trap you here forever."

We all decide to see what was happening in the other classrooms and to see if we could find anybody.

We all split up, John goes to Year 6, Molly goes to Year 3, Chandler goes to Year 2, and I go to the Staff Room.

I shout, "Let's all meet back at the Rugby field and be careful."

Chapter 7 – John's Quest

John trudges off slowly to Year 6, inside he is feeling very afraid, but he's doing his best to hide it.

The Year 6 door keeps opening and shutting on its own. The wind is getting stronger, and it is pushing John towards the door.

As the door blows wide open, a massive gust of wind blows John through the door.

BANG!!! The door slams shut trapping John's foot.

John screams out in pain, "Help, help me."

John isn't aware that the Year 6 classroom is soundproof.

He feels a tugging on his foot whilst it is trapped in the door.

John looks round and there is nothing there, but he can still feel his foot being tugged.

He uses all his strength and pulls his leg free; his leg is throbbing with pain.

John sees the black hooded figure outside the classroom, then it teleports into the classroom next to him.

The figure just stares at John.

"What do you want from me?" says John.

The figure just teleports away again.

John begins to look around for the hooded figure, as he can't believe it has just disappeared.

But he can't find any clues about where the hooded figure has gone.

Then suddenly John is sat chained to a school chair with a desk in front of him and the hooded figure to the side.

The hooded figure says in a scary voice, "Now right ten thousand lines saying I will not investigate, or my friends will be hurt."

John sighs deeply and begins writing the lines so his friends would not be hurt.

Chapter 8 –
Molly's Quest

Molly starts to sprint towards Year 3, her heart is pounding with fear.

Molly arrives at the Year 3 classroom door which is wide open, she nervously steps through.

BANG! The classroom door slams shut behind her.

The black hooded figure suddenly appears behind Molly and points to the corner of the classroom.

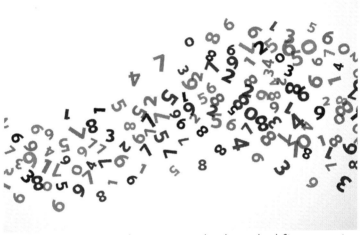

Molly is too scared to move, the hooded figure grips Molly's arm and leads her to the corner of the classroom where all the reading books are kept.

All the tables in the classroom begin moving on their own and trap Molly in the corner.

The floor starts to rumble and with a big thump Molly falls to the floor.

The hooded figure walks over to Molly and says in an angry voice, "You must count aloud to a million or I will hurt your friends."

Molly gulps deeply and begins counting, "1, 2, 3, 4 ………………"

Chapter 9 – Chandler's Quest

Chandler briskly walks to the Year 2 classroom. He looks around nervously.

He looks through the window and can't see anyone. So, he heads into the classroom.

As Chandler gets into the Year 2 classroom, he can hear a faint crying noise coming from the store cupboard.

He asks, "Who's there, are you ok?"

There is no response so Chandler walks into the large unlit cupboard.

The door shuts behind him and he feels somebody grab his arm.

He sees a small black figure through the darkness.

He hears a quiet screeching voice say, "Who are you? Who are you? Who are you?"

Each time the voice gets quieter and quieter until it becomes a whisper.

Then the voice says, "Get out of the cupboard or you might be punished like me."

Chandler asks, "What are the punishments?"

The girl whispers, "Being tied up together against a wooden log."

Suddenly Chandler finds himself standing upright tied to a log and he can feel that someone else is tied up too.

It's the girl, but Chandler can't see who it is.

Chandler wriggles and squirms and manages to release one arm. Meanwhile, the girl Chandler is tied to is being sucked up through the mouth of the black hooded figure.

Chandler sees the black figure in front of him, and with all his strength he punches the figure in the head with his free arm.

The black hooded figure feels a wave of anger run through it and growls loudly, then teleports away.

Chandler faints on to the floor of the cupboard.

Chapter 10 - Harry's Quest

I run towards the Staff Room as quickly as I can.

As soon as I get to the hallway, I have to climb on the bookshelves to avoid the big hole that was created earlier.

I move cautiously sideways across the bookshelves. As I do the floor starts to come towards me, as all the books are stacking up on top of each other.

Then the books begin to move, but I am too scared to jump to safety. I hesitate and then slip into the big hole.

I am falling deeper and deeper into the hole, I see part of my life flash before my eyes.

Then with a massive thud, I hit the lava that is at the bottom of the hole. This time the floor really is lava.

As soon as I hit the lava, I close my eyes. The lava is hot and feels uncomfortable for about 18 seconds, then the heat disappears.

I open my eyes I can see that the floor is a purply black colour and the walls are white.

The ceiling above me is filled with magical art and pictures of mythical creatures. There are some which are very bright and colourful and others that are very dark and dull.

As I lie on the ground, I realise I'm not hurt despite the long fall. I even notice that my arm I injured earlier no longer hurts.

It seems that during the fall my arm was somehow repaired.

As I continue to lie on the floor, I begin to feel stronger and stronger, my eyesight seems sharper, and I have an unusual feeling all over my body. My energy levels are very high.

Then I hear the mumblings of different voices in my head saying, "Are you here for our help?"

I squint through the darkness, and I see a big green and white Griffin directly in front of me, I can feel its warm breath on my cheeks.

I can also see a colossal blue and black hairy monster.

I continue to look round I see an extremely tall unicorn with a long horn. The unicorn gently pushes its nose against my face and says, "Are you ok?"

Then I see a lion with a black mane and elegant scaly tail, it is like a merlion, this is an image that would scare almost anyone away.

With some fear in my voice, I call out, "Are you real or am I imagining you?"

The lion with the scaly tail calls back "Everything starts in your imagination, but it is up to you if you want to make it real."

Chapter 11 –
The Truth Grasped

I know I have to make this real, me and my friends need all the help we can get.

The unicorn asks me, "Do you know how to make this real?"

I said, "No, but I've got a feeling that I can work it out."

I close my eyes again and spend a few minutes imagining that the crazy mysterious creatures are real.

I imagine playing with the creatures and also imagine them helping me to solve the mystery at the school.

It begins to feel like I may be able to really succeed at my magical quest.

I call all of the creatures around me, and I say, "I need your help to get out of here. How do I get back to a normal life?"

The unicorn answers in a high-pitched smooth voice, "You just have to imagine it, believe with all your heart and make it become real."

I think for a minute about what do I want to make real.

I want to make sure John, Chandler and Molly are safe. I also want the school to be back in one piece and all the missing children to come back.

The big blue and black hairy monster whispers in a deep shy voice, "For everything you want to make real, you have to complete a ....!!!"

Suddenly I continue to fall down and down. "NNNNNNNOOOOOOOOOOOOO, what do I need to complete?" I scream.

The Griffin's voice is muffled by my screams as he tries to explain.

Then THUMP! I've hit the ground but this time I am all alone.

I look around, and it appears that I have landed in the middle of an obstacle course.

I see there is a pool of liquid nitrogen underneath me, and its rising fast. I need to move quickly, as it is freezing cold.

Chapter 12 - Obstacle Course

The first obstacle is a floating platform that is moving in thin air.

I think to myself, "Wait a second, if I can imagine this is not real. Maybe I won't die if I fall into the liquid nitrogen pool."

I leap on to the platform with ease and I see in the distance some jump pads that keep fading in and out of reality.

I carefully jump across a large gap to the next platform.

I notice the platform behind me start to fade away, so I just keep jumping from platform to platform and eventually reach the last but one platform.

I manage to grab it with my fingertips. I'm hanging and slowly start to freeze; I can feel the ice on my fingers and my hair starts to go stiff.

I'm in trouble, I'm going to die if I can't get out of here quick.

I suddenly recall what the Unicorn said to me, "You just have to imagine it, believe with all your heart and make it become real."

I start to imagine a temperature gauge. I see that it is saying the temperature is zero degrees centigrade.

I imagine the temperature on the gauge slowly rising from 1 degree to 5 degrees, to 10 degrees.

I begin to warm up and I get the feeling back in my fingers and I manage to swing and jump to the last platform, and I immediately fall through it.

Chapter 13 – Chandler's Challenge

I land with a THUD! I look around to get my bearings. I'm in a cupboard and can see a body next to me face down.

I think I recognise that scruffy haircut, I walk towards the body, I can see it faintly breathing.

I call out to the body, "Chandler is that you?" I get no response.

I call out again, "Where are we Chandler?", still nothing.

I roll over the body and am both happy and startled. It is my friend Chandler, but he is unconscious with his eyes open, and they are very still.

All of sudden Chandler sits bolt upright and he starts to quack like a duck, "Quack, quack, quack!"

I ask him, "What are you doing Chandler?"

Chandler then lays down with his arms straight down beside him and he starts to shake like crazy.

I'm very worried and shout out, "How can I help him?"

Then I hear in my head the Green and White Griffin say, "Your friend has been hypnotised by the black hooded figure, the only way you can break him out of it is to make him laugh."

"Your friend has been hypnotised by the black hooded figure, the only way you can break him out of it is to make him laugh."

"That's easy, I can always make Chandler laugh. Thank you, Griffin," I say.

I rack my brain and come up with my best joke.

"Why did the Cyclops close his school? Because he only had one pupil."

A slight smile appears on Chandler's face then I hear a giggle that turns into a roar of laughter.

Chandler sits up and says, "Harry it is so good to see you, but is that really your best joke."

We both fall over with laughter and relief, and I explain that we will need to do a challenge to save Molly.

Chapter 14 – Molly's Maze

I kick open the cupboard door that Chandler had been trapped in.

To our amazement we are in the middle of a field and in front of us is a maze made of deep green, very tall evergreen bushes. In the middle is a very tall brick tower, with a sign over the top saying 'The Finish'.

At the front of the bushes was a gap with a wooden banner over the top saying 'Start Here'.

I say to Chandler. "This must be our challenge, are you ready to go?"

Chandler says, "Last time I did one of these, I got lost for hours and had to be rescued."

We enter the Maze and begin walking to our left. We repeatedly hit dead ends.

Next, we go left, then right, right, right, left, right. We finally think we are getting somewhere as we were right next to the brick tower. We take the final left turn.

"Damn," we both say.

We are faced with another green bush dead end, as we turn around to go back, we can see that we are surrounded by evergreen bushes on all sides.

There are no exits, we have been trapped.

I say to Chandler, "Get on my shoulders and let's climb over the bushes."

Chandler gets on my shoulders, but as he does the bushes grow taller, and taller, and taller, and taller.

Is this where we will meet our end.

A very large Tree monster appears in front of us and Chandler screams, "Don't eat me!"

I explain that the monsters have been helping me and I ask the monster, "What we should do?"

The monster replies in a shy gravelly voice "Imagine you are free, and the bushes cannot hold you."

"Imagine you are free, and the bushes cannot hold you."

"But the bushes are so thick and high," says Chandler.

"Then we must imagine them to be something else," I say.

We talk about what we can imagine. Chandler suggests the biggest door in the world that everyone can fit through.

But in the end, we agree we would imagine a large open archway. We hold hands, take a bit of a run up and use all our powers to imagine the large open archway.

Just as we hit the archway and get smacked in the face by a lot of green foliage, we are then the other side of the bushes, standing before the brick tower.

We slowly and carefully climb up the wooden ladder inside the tower. Close up, the tower looks even taller than before.

I count each step. 323, 324, 325 and it still doesn't look like we are even a quarter of the way to the top.

Suddenly I get an image of Molly counting, 17012, 17013, 17014. She looks nervous and sounds breathless as she counts.

I keep counting 2297, 2298, 2299. Eventually, after what seems like hours, we reach the top of the ladder.

Above us is a wooden hatch. It is made of an old heavy oakwood with a brass handle.

I push open the hatch with a strong shoulder barge. The hatch door creaks loudly as it opens.

I set foot into the small wooden room and as Chandler follows me in, we jump on the Helter Skelter slide at the other side of the room.

Chapter 15 – Counting on Molly

We go flying down the slide, faster and faster, getting dizzier and dizzier.

I shout out to Chandler, "We must be going over 100mph! If we don't slow down, we are going to fly off the end at the bottom."

I am right, as we hit the end we do fly through the sky.

"AAAAAARRRRRRGGGGGGGHHHHH!" we both scream as we fly through the air.

As we land, we bash into a lot of school desks and chairs. We are bruised but not broken.

We shake off the heavy fall, and both see Molly sat in the corner counting.

"21259, 21260, 21261," Molly continues to count.

"Molly it is so good to see you," I say.

Molly says nothing but keeps counting.

"Can't you see us Molly," says Chandler.

Molly glares at us and puts a finger to her lips,

"Quiet I will lose count and the black hooded figure will hurt us," she says.

"I have to count to a million or the black hooded figure will hurt us all," Molly continues.

I shouted, "I have an idea, try this, 1, 2, miss a few, 999999, 1000000."

Molly has lost count, so copies my idea.

"1, 2, miss a few, 999999, 1000000" she says.

Then immediately the furniture goes back to where it should be, and we stand up and head towards the classroom door.

From the other side of the classroom, we hear the black hooded figure shout out angrily, "You have completed your tasks, but not the way I wanted you to!"

I shout back, "We found a better way to do it. Now leave us alone."

I slam the door behind us, and I explain to Molly about all the Quests and the help the monsters and mythical creatures have given us.

We agree we should go to the Year 6 classroom to see if we can find John.

Chapter 16 – The Key to Reunite Us All

We run towards the Year 6 classroom as quickly as we can. We are nervous that the black hooded figure may appear at any point.

We are relieved to reach the classroom but are shocked when we see a massive rusty padlock securing the door.

Next to it is an equally massive bunch of metal keys. There are hundreds of them.

Molly picks up the keyring and starts to try each of the keys.

The first key won't go in the lock. The second key fits the lock but won't turn.

We carry on until we had tried the first hundred keys.

All the keys on the keyring begin to shake and suddenly the lion with the scaly tail appears.

The lion says, "You don't need to try every key, but you do have to face up to the reality of your situation."

The lion carries on "Don't choose the correct key, let the correct key choose you."

We all sit down on the floor and put the bunch of keys in front of us.

We sit and watch for a few minutes, hoping the correct key will choose us.

As we sit and wait the sun comes out from behind the clouds and starts to stream through the classroom windows.

It strikes a small silver key which begins to shimmer and shine. It then begins to gently vibrate.

I grab the key and shout, "This is the one, it has chosen us."

I placed the silver key into the lock and without even turning the key, the lock opens, and we are into the Year 6 classroom.

In the corner of the classroom, we can see John chained to a desk in a glass box.

Chapter 17 - John and Gone

We rush over to John; he is still writing lines.

I say, "John, we are here to rescue you."

John smiles and says, "I am chained to the chair, and in this box, I can't get free."

I show John the key we had used to get past the door, "This is a very special key, watch," I say.

I put the key next to the padlock that is keeping John's glass box locked and his chains in place. The key changes shape to fit the padlock and immediately the chains fall away.

We all stand up and hug and cheer. Then we hear the black hooded figure shout, "You haven't completed your task. I warned you that I will harm your friends."

The black hooded figure tries to hit us with a large wooden cane. It just goes over John's head.

Then we hear the whisper of the Unicorn, "The black hooded figure is just in pain; it feels unloved and scared. It is made up of all the energy of any child who has had a bad or tricky day at school."

The Unicorn continues, "Show it kindness and friendship and things can change."

"Show it kindness and friendship and things can change."

Chapter 18 – From Bad to Good

The black hooded figure tries to hit us with the stick again. It strikes Chandler on the arm.

I shout out, "I am Harry, what is your name?"

Molly shouts, "What games do you like to play?"

The black hooded figure stops throwing its cane around and looks confused.

John asks, "Do you have any friends that you can play with?"

Chandler says, "You can play with us."

Out on the school playing field is an old ball, Molly runs over and picks it up. She tosses it over towards the hooded figure and gestures to kick it.

The hooded figure kicks the ball towards John and John kicks it back.

We all carry on kicking the ball for about 5 minutes. Then all of a sudden, the figure pulls back its hood to reveal a sad looking young girl with brown eyes and medium length brown hair in a ponytail.

The girl says, "My name is Hope, and I have always hoped that one day someone would ask me my name."

With that the girl disappears and leaves behind the black hooded cloak on the floor in a pile.

Once again, the sun starts shining and everything around us seems to sparkle.

The four of us are quite shocked with what has just happened and how sad the hooded girl had been

Chapter 19 – Back to Normal

We walk back across the field towards the school buildings. We chat about what an incredibly strange day we had all been through.

As we glance up at the buildings, we noticed that all the damage has been repaired, there are no signs of the earlier problems.

We head to the school hall, as we get there, we can hear someone speaking.

It's Cool
to Be Kind!

It is our Head Teacher giving an assembly, "......and remember everyone this is National Be Kind day," she says.

We smile when we hear this and burst through the hall doors. All the school students are sat in rows of chairs facing towards the Head Teacher. Everyone has been returned safely.

The Head Teacher glares at us and shouts, "Harry, John, Chandler and Molly, you are all late for assembly. That's detention for all of you for the rest of the week."

The End

(For Now)